KYLE B. ...

CARTOONIST

KYLE BAKER PUBLISHING
NEW YORK, 2004

KYLE

CARTO

KYLE BAKER PUBLISHING

NEW YORK, 2004

WWW.KYLEBAKER.COM

BAKER
ONIST

For Dad

KYLE BAKER CARTOONIST
copyright 2004 by Kyle Baker

Published by
KYLE BAKER PUBLISHING
P.O. Box 1400 Woodstock, NY 12498

visit www.kylebaker.com

I S B N 0-9747214-0-9

First printing 2004
10 9 8 7 6 5 4 3 2 1

Printed in Canada

Thanks to:
Jeff Smith and Vijaya Iyer of Cartoon Books
Eddie Campbell
David and Maria Lapham of El Capitán

KYLE BAKER

DIRECTIONS
How To Read This Book

CONGRATULATIONS!

0 0 40 60 80 100

KYLE BAKER

Entertainment Meter Company, Inc.
The Coolest Place Ever, U.S.A.

THE **OFFICIAL** ENTERTAINMENT
METER RATING FOR THIS VOLUME IS:

100

~An Important Message From The Publisher~

When Kyle asked me to write a forward for *Cartoonist*, I thought, "No way. I am way too sleep-deprived." (We had our third baby just two days ago!) But I did want to share with you readers just how much fun it has been living with Kyle while he created this book.

While working on graphic novels or animation projects at home, Kyle rarely solicits my opinion. Occasionally, in his quest for visual clarity, he shows me a drawing and asks if I understand what is happening. But with *Cartoonist* I was his focus group, his humor-level guinea pig. "I've got another one for you," he'd say, showing me his latest cartoon. These presentations have been a daily delight; virtually every cartoon has made me laugh out loud, particularly the ones about our family.

"Kyle," I asked him recently, "How do you do it? How do you keep making up these hilarious cartoons day after day?" His reply:

"We get a bill, we have to pay it, I write a joke." There you have it.

Cartoonist is Kyle's first self-publishing venture, and, I believe, his best book to date. These two facts are not unrelated: the freedom to create controversial material - without worrying about offending the sensibilities of a large publisher - has been artistically liberating. But of course, I am financially biased: as a self-publisher, every copy of *Cartoonist* sold helps pay those bills.

"What else do you want me to write?" I ask Kyle.

"Tell them what it's like living with me."

A picture is worth a thousand words: Read *The Bakers*.

Cheers,

ELIZABETH GLASS

Boss, Kyle Baker Publishing

"Freddie Morris! You haven't aged a day!"

"Yesh?"

"About China-- We don't use the phrase, 'child labor', we say, 'By Kids, For Kids'."

"Why is it the rich ones are always single?"

"I still panic when I see those lights flashing in the rear view, but then I remember--That's my motorcade!"

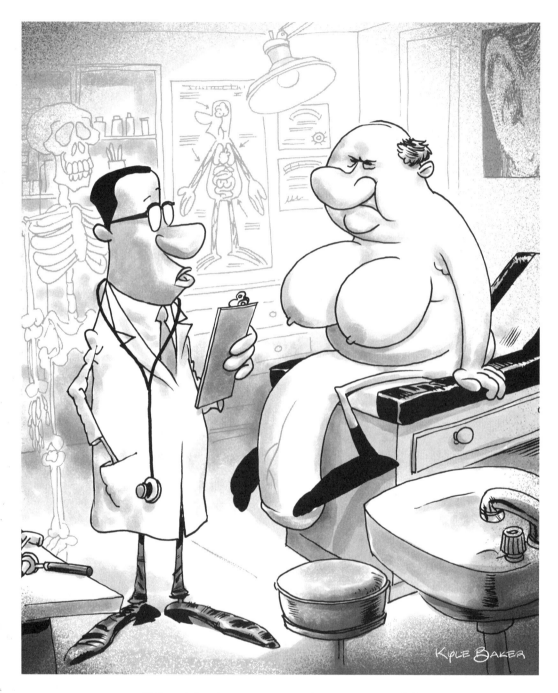

"My advice is, stop answering your e-mail."

"You call yourself a suicide bomber?"

"Are you going to wear that?"

"--As long as you don't make me look like Pat Buchanan."

"Okay! I admit it! File sharing is stealing! Can I go now?"

"I think we should see other people."

Doggie porn.

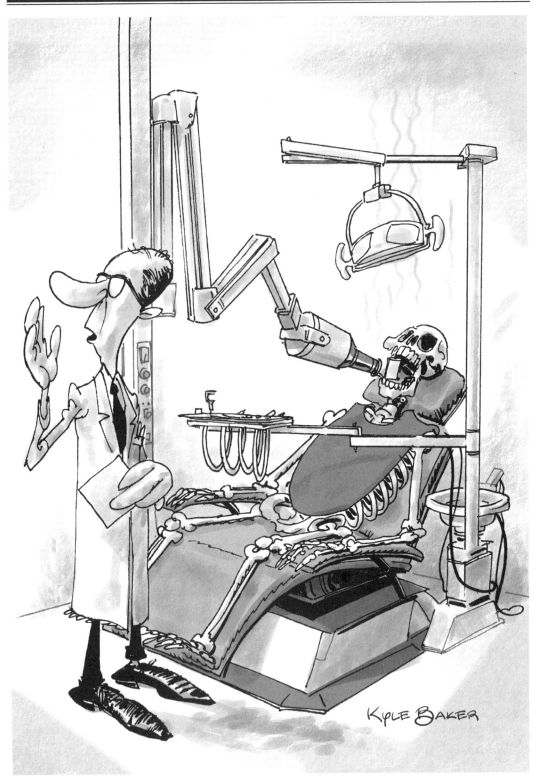

"Oh, and Maria, call someone about getting the x-ray adjusted."

"Look at the bright side. A year ago, we'd never even <u>heard</u> of market timing."

"Stop following me!"

"I've been thinking... How come when it gets cold, we have to get naked?"

"I need a hug."

Elephant's graveyard, my eye! This is the elephant's crack house!
I told you that map was a fake!

Rejected Rorschach Blots

Kyle Baker

Poem

～ PLEA FOR PIECE ～

I hate everybody,
Hate them day and night.
Everybody hates me too,
The difference is, I'm right.

-Rumi
(translated but not read)

The Ladder

MORE ☞

KYLE BAKER

THE HOUR

MORE

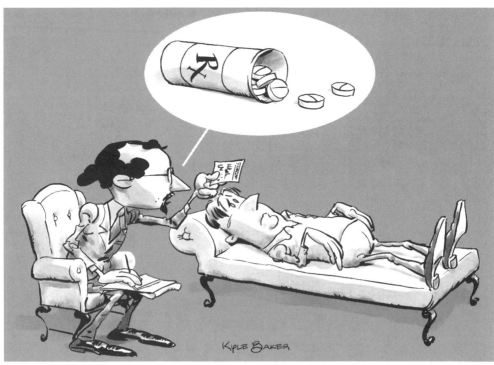

Beauty

More 👉

KYLE BAKER

Once Upon A Time

KYLE BAKER

THE BOOK

"Not if you were the last male elephant on earth."

"About shoulder length. Why do you ask?"

SWEET SUE, Defense Attorney

"Objection! Prosecution is leading the witness!"

"Now remember, let me do all the talking."

THE PENILE

"Calm down. You're not being executed, I'm in here for molesting parishioners."

"I caught my wife eating crackers in bed, so I killed them."

Myrna Burner, Psychonaut.

"All right, who's the wise guy?"

"That's such a gorgeous drawing. Seems almost a shame to eat it."

Memories

MORE ☞

KYLE BAKER

CORN ON MACABRE

"Look! A boat! We're saved!"

"See? __That's__ the kind of cape I was talking about."

THE BAKERS

As my lovely wife Liz mentioned at the beginning of this compendium, our third baby, Jackie,was born just a few days before CARTOONIST went to press. While dear Jackie is represented on the title page of this section, and in one cartoon drawn after her birth, she is conspicuously absent from the rest of these cartoons.

I mention this because my oldest daughter Lil has been very conscious of how many cartoons she appears in compared to her brother Ike. When I draw a cartoon which features only Ike, I must quickly execute one featuring only Lil, lest I suffer her wrath. I assume that as soon as Jackie's old enough to read, she'll demand equal time.

These cartoons are not printed chronologically. I arranged them more for the sake of pacing and storytelling. Some of the jokes work better once you understand the characters, so I moved them to later pages. Because of this, you may notice that the characters change appearance from strip to strip, most noticeably the character of Ike, who is only two years old and has grown considerably over the months it took me to draw this book.

Liz once asked me why I draw myself so fat. I explained that fat is funny. Daughter Lil asked why I draw Mommy so skinny. I explained it's because Daddy's no fool. Over the months I've been trying to draw myself dumber and fatter each time, and my nose bigger. I thank Liz for permission to draw her nose much bigger than it is. I don't know many women who would tolerate such treatment. Liz even suggested I do some gags about the pregnancy, but any man who's made fun of a pregnant lady can tell you how smart that would have been. I'll do those jokes in a future book, along with a bunch of cartoons about baby Jackie.

Without further adieu, ladies and gentlemen, meet *the Bakers*.

DADDY'S TIME

MORE 👉

KYLE BAKER

Dress The Baby

More 🖐

More 👉

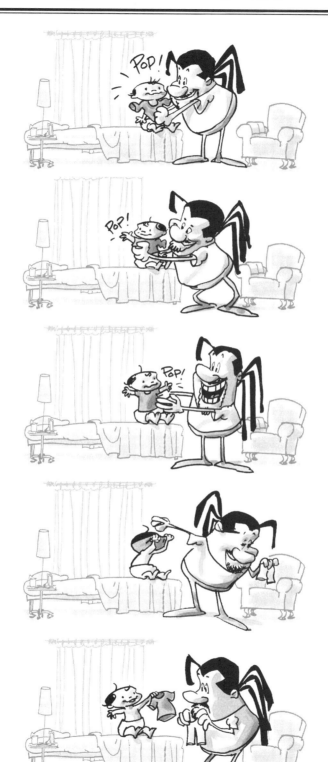

Kyle Baker

Butt Joke

KYLE BAKER

FALL

MORE

KYLE BAKER

Gift

KYLE BAKER

"We're not lost. We just passed the corner of Shutup and Letme Drive."

Nose

More

KYLE BAKER

THE FAIR

MORE ☜

MORE

KYLE BAKER

Daddy Helps

KYLE BAKER

More

KYLE BAKER

DIET

MORE 👉

KYLE BAKER

LIL *And* DAD'S MOVIE REVIEWS

 **Theater 1**

Theater 2 →

CARNAGE

Precious Pixies

MORE

KYLE BAKER

❧ Explorer ❧

KYLE BAKER

MASTER IKE'S
Toddler Self-Defense

LESSON ONE: *The Bridge*

The bridge, in quiet strength, supports the traveler even as it directs his course.

The bridge achieves this by doing nothing.

1.
Begin by quieting the self and finding your center. Be as the earth.

2.
Raise your center. Distribute your energy throughout the arch. Become a bridge.

More 👉

The Bridge

This powerful fighting technique
confounds the opponent who attempts
to imprison you in a car seat. The
technique is most effective in
conjunction with a battle scream.

More

LESSON TWO: *The Water*

Water is passive, always flowing downhill.
When contained, it takes the shape of its
container. It can be broken by a blade of grass.

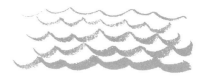

Yet water can hold up a battleship, or tear
down a mountain. It is the source of life.

Be like water.

1.
Quiet the self.
Focus your chi.
Breathe deeply.

2.
Exhale slowly,
expelling all tension
with each breath.
Become like water.

More

The Water

This fighting technique is mighty. Like the ocean, you cannot be directed or controlled. The opponent who seeks to take you where you do not wish to go will be thwarted.

More 👉

LESSON THREE: *The Tree*

The tree appears to do nothing. In reality, it is constantly building its strength.

Silently, slowly, it digs itself deeper into the earth, becoming unmovable. Its trunk grows thicker each year, its branches expand to capture more energy from the sun.

Thus do the sun and earth become the tree's servants.

1.
Quiet the self.
Extend your arms.
Inhale, growing rigid.

Become the tree.

More 🐾

The Tree

Lao Tzu says, "The opponent who cannot undress you cannot bathe you."

You are undefeatable.

KYLE BAKER

Art

More 🖐

KYLE BAKER

LIGHTS OUT!

Look at this! Why is every light in the house on all night? The kids are asleep! Not even unconsciousness deters them from their their important work of bankrupting me.

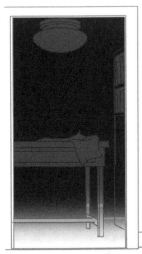

You people think I'm the U.S. mint. "Oh, don't worry, Daddy'll just make more money! It flows from his drawing pen like ink!

Bad enough you have the lights on all day while sunlight cascades through our huge uninsulated windows, but to illuminate empty rooms all night! I mean, if you don't want me to ever be able to retire, just *say* so!

MORE

MORE

Meditation

More 🐾

Health

KYLE BAKER

Story

KYLE BAKER

Break

More 🐎

More ☞

OVERHEARD

DAREDEVIL

MORE

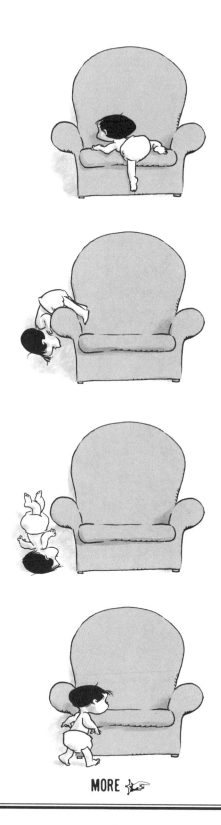

MORE 👉

"I'm telling."

THE KYLE BAKER INSTITUTE FOR ADULT EDUCATION

presents

An Exclusive Four-Day Seminar

HOW TO REMOVE A JUMP ROPE FROM A SLINKY

Seating is limited. Call for reservations.

THANKS FOR READING!

ENJOY THESE OTHER BOOKS BY

Kyle Baker

Why I Hate Saturn

The Cowboy Wally Show

You Are Here

I Die At Midnight

King David

Undercover Genie